ARE YOU A PUZZLE MASTER?

Susan, Matt, Tom, and their little dog, Patches, are always on the lookout for new adventures. That's why they will be visiting the museum exhibit of dazzling treasures collected by Leo Panthera, a world-famous explorer.

Jacob, a guide at the museum, has invited his four friends to go along with him on a special tour before the exhibit opens. Susan, Matt, Tom, and Patches will not only see the exhibit, but also join Leo in his adventures— *through their imaginations.* Be sure to look for Leo—he's there, somewhere, in each adventure!

A Reader's Digest Kids Book
Published by The Reader's Digest Association, Inc.
Produced by Joshua Morris Publishing, Inc.
Copyright © 1991 John Speirs
With additional text by Gill Speirs
All rights reserved. Unauthorized reproduction, in
any manner, is prohibited.

Library of Congress Cataloging in Publication Data
Speirs, John.
    The quest for the golden mane / John Speirs.

       p. cm.—(Puzzle masters)
    Summary: A series of picture puzzles in which the reader helps
three young Puzzle Masters and their dog search for hidden treasure
while dealing with tunnels, caves, forged treasures and maps, a
maze, and other obstacles.

    ISBN 0-89577-394-5

    1. Maze puzzles—Juvenile literature. [I. Picture puzzles.
2. Puzzles.] I. Title. II. Series
GV1507. M3S67 1991
793.73–dc20
                                    91-33894
                                      CIP
                                      AC

READER'S DIGEST and the Pegasus logo are registered trademarks of The Reader's Digest Association, Inc.
Printed in Hong Kong

John Speirs
?PUZZLE MASTERS
The Quest for the Golden Mane

Reader's Digest Kids
PLEASANTVILLE, N.Y. – MONTREAL

MUSEUM QUEST

Great excitement ripples through the huge crowd waiting in the central hall of the museum. Everyone wants to be among the first to see the fantastic treasures collected by Leo Panthera.

"I had no idea there'd be so many people here today," Susan whispers to herself. Then she looks down at her watch. "Oh, no," she cries. "I'm late!"

Susan is supposed to meet Tom, Matt, Patches, and Jacob in the central hall. But where are they?

Help Susan find her way through the maze of people to Jacob. She must pick up Matt, Tom, and Patches before she reaches Jacob—without retracing her steps. And don't forget to look for Leo!

AZTEC CRYSTAL MYSTERY

Jacob leads the adventurers to a glass case that holds a glittering crystal lion's skull.

"This is unique," he explains. "Finding it, after so many had failed, shot Leo to fame!"

"Where did he find it?" asks Matt.

"Deep in a dark, steamy, tropical jungle of central Mexico," says Jacob. "Leo hacked a path through the jungle, winding past all kinds of dangerous animals."

"Was he alone?" breathes Tom.

"Not at first," says Jacob. "But his guides disappeared, one by one. Leo refused to give up. Finally, he reached an ancient Aztec temple. There was the treasure: a crystal lion's skull flashing like fire in the sun. But before he could succeed, Leo had to find a path through the maze of the pyramid."

Can you find the route Leo took to reach the crystal lion's skull? Watch out for the wild animals hiding in the jungle. Can you find eleven of them?

START HERE ▶

THE TWIN JADE LIONS OF THE WAN TU

"Two identical jade lions were the symbol of the Wan Tu people and were very precious to them," begins Jacob. "The outlawed Tong gang were the sworn enemies of the Wan Tu. The Tongs wanted to destroy the lions and take over Wan Tu City!"

"What happened?" asks Susan.

"The Wan Tu emperor asked Leo to take the lions to the museum to protect them. The emperor opened the city gates to let Leo in. But a Tong spy changed the characters on four of the banners outside the city's wall. That was a signal to the Tongs that the gates were open. Five Tongs sneaked in, too!"

"Wan Tu City looks like a strange place!" says Tom. "Are the people on top walking up or down?"

"It's a real Chinese puzzle," agrees Jacob, "as Leo found out when he tried to rescue the lions."

Can you pick out the two identical jade lions—and the five Tongs dressed in black who are trying to destroy them?

THE LION'S EYE OF INDIA

"Is a lion's eye really so rare?" asks Matt.

"This one is," laughs Jacob. "It's the largest emerald in the world."

"What's the story?" asks Tom.

"The Lion's Eye was once the property of an Indian rajah," answers Jacob. "But it was stolen by a rival and hidden in one of three statues in a ruined temple."

"Why couldn't the rajah get it back?" asks Matt.

"It was guarded at all times by a slithering mass of poisonous snakes," says Jacob. "The rajah was amazed when Leo found a way over the snakes to recapture the emerald."

One of the statues looks a little different from the other two. That is where the Lion's Eye was hidden. To get there, Leo crossed over the snakes, moving from tail to head to another tail — not giving them a chance to snap! See if you can trace the path Leo took to the emerald and back again.

THE TREASURE OF THE *SANTA MORTE*

"Now this is a good story," says Jacob, rubbing his hands together. "The pirate ship *Santa Morte*, its hold filled with gold, was lost at sea in a fierce storm. For centuries, the ship and its precious cargo lay at the bottom of the sea. Sharks, stingrays, and moray eels scared off anyone who came near.

"But one day, Leo and a group of brave divers armed with spear guns, knives, and stun darts fought their

way to the ship. There they found treasure
even more fabulous than they had ever
imagined!"

Can you find the treasure of the Santa Morte?
Look for ten golden coins, a golden saber, a
jeweled chalice, a diamond ring, a treasure chest
key, and a golden crown. Can you also find at
least ten things wrong with this picture?

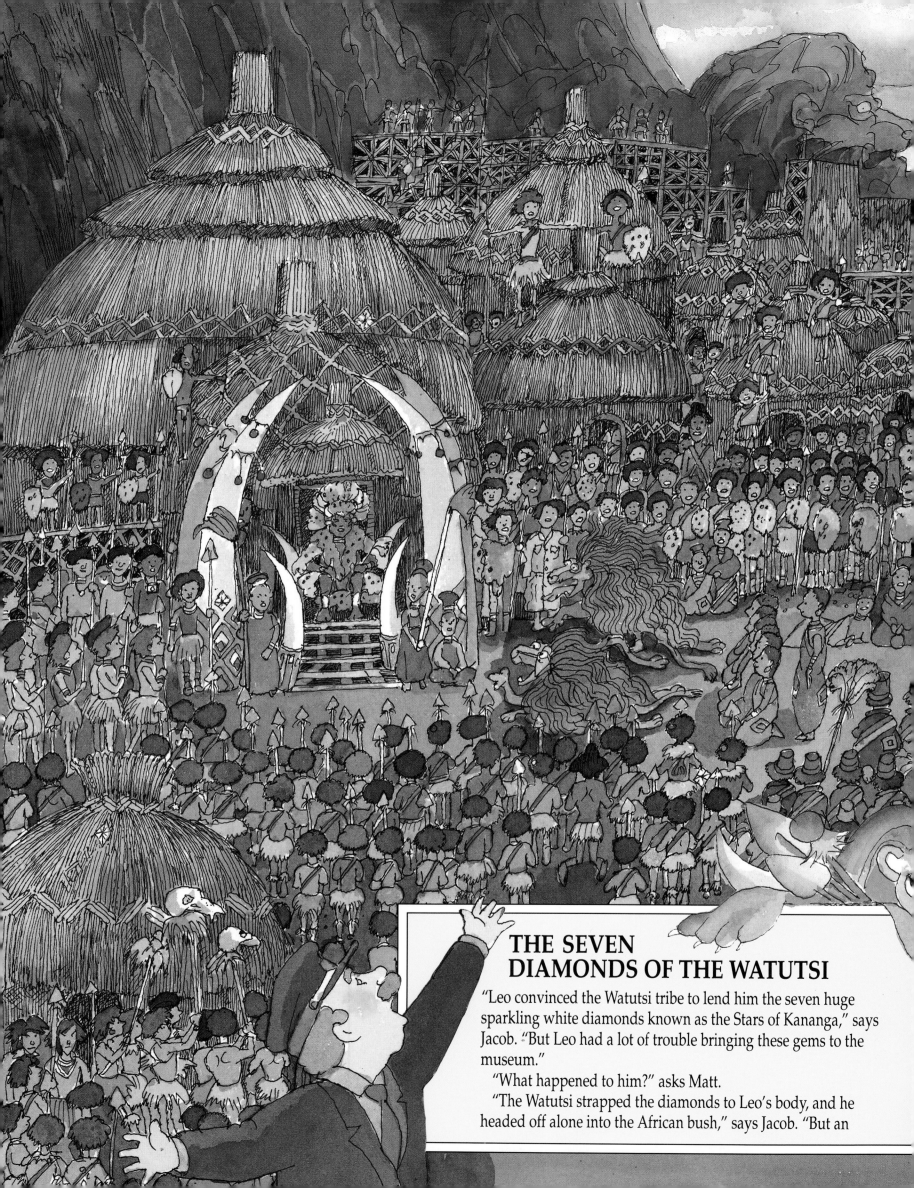

THE SEVEN DIAMONDS OF THE WATUTSI

"Leo convinced the Watutsi tribe to lend him the seven huge sparkling white diamonds known as the Stars of Kananga," says Jacob. "But Leo had a lot of trouble bringing these gems to the museum."

"What happened to him?" asks Matt.

"The Watutsi strapped the diamonds to Leo's body, and he headed off alone into the African bush," says Jacob. "But an

enemy tribe ambushed him, took him prisoner, and stole the diamonds! Leo thought he would be killed. But five tall Watutsi scouts crept unnoticed into the enemy village. They helped him recover the diamonds and escape!"

Can you find the five Watutsi who came to help Leo? Leo lost his clothes...shirt, socks, pants, shoes, and safari coat. He also lost his eye patch and camera, as well as the diamonds. Can you find all of them?

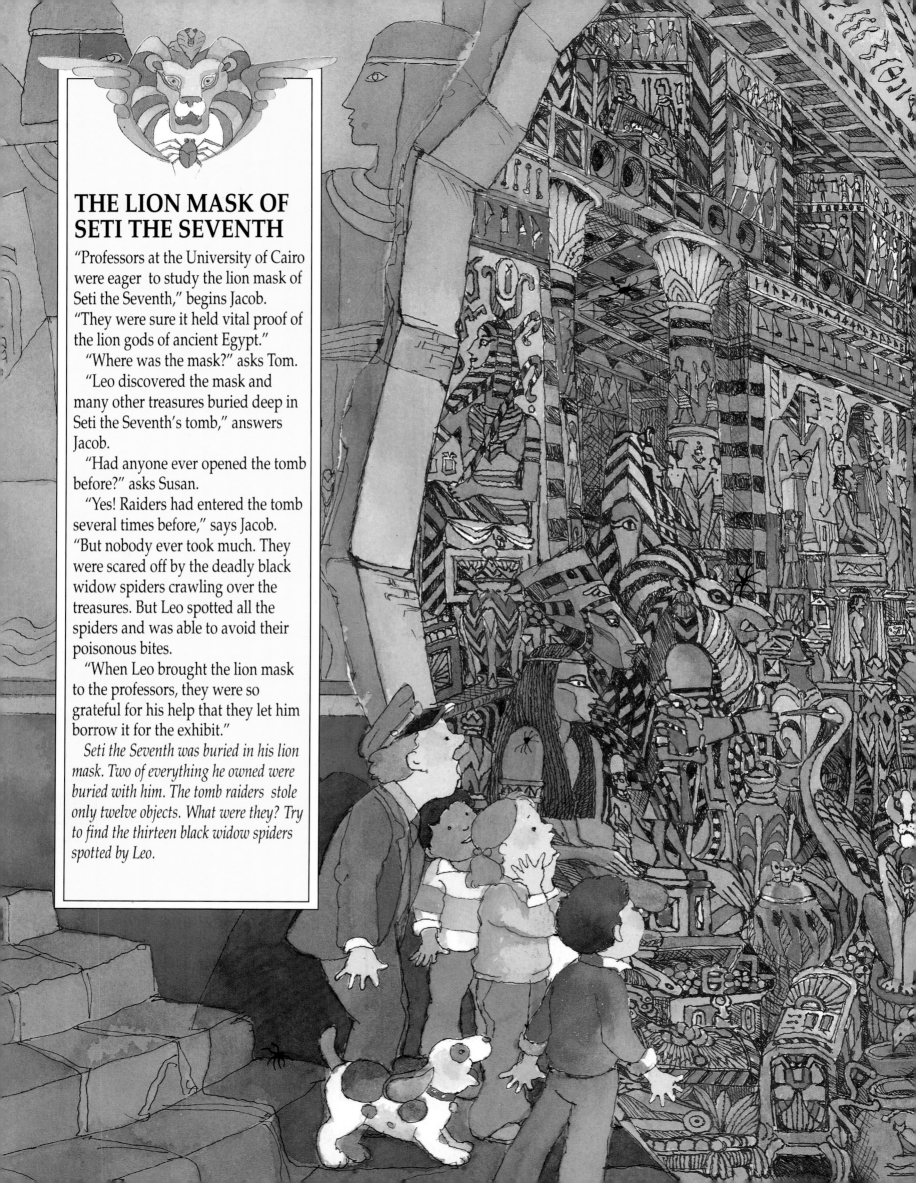

THE LION MASK OF SETI THE SEVENTH

"Professors at the University of Cairo were eager to study the lion mask of Seti the Seventh," begins Jacob. "They were sure it held vital proof of the lion gods of ancient Egypt."

"Where was the mask?" asks Tom.

"Leo discovered the mask and many other treasures buried deep in Seti the Seventh's tomb," answers Jacob.

"Had anyone ever opened the tomb before?" asks Susan.

"Yes! Raiders had entered the tomb several times before," says Jacob. "But nobody ever took much. They were scared off by the deadly black widow spiders crawling over the treasures. But Leo spotted all the spiders and was able to avoid their poisonous bites.

"When Leo brought the lion mask to the professors, they were so grateful for his help that they let him borrow it for the exhibit."

Seti the Seventh was buried in his lion mask. Two of everything he owned were buried with him. The tomb raiders stole only twelve objects. What were they? Try to find the thirteen black widow spiders spotted by Leo.

THE CHALICE OF RICHARD THE LION-HEARTED

Matt, Susan, and Tom stare at a glittering gold and amber cup.

"Beautiful as it looks, this chalice was believed to have terrible powers," says Jacob. "The knights of King Richard the Lion-Hearted were so afraid of it that they hid it deep down in a secret chamber."

"How did Leo ever find it?" asks Matt.

"Only after a long, difficult search," answers Jacob.

DEVIL EYE CAVE: EXIT TO TWIN CAVE

TUNNEL CAVE: EXIT TO DRAGON CAVE

STALACTITE MAZE CAVERN: EXIT TO MASK GROTTO

SENTINEL GROTTO: EXIT TO DOUBLE GATE GROTTO

TREASURE CANYON: EXIT TO NEEDLE EYE CAVE

SKULL GORGE: EXIT TO DOUBLE GATE GROTTO

BLUE GROTTO: EXIT TO FIRE-FLY CAVERN

ROSE QUARTZ CAVERN: EXIT TO GREEN GATE CAVERN

PIRATE GORGE: EXIT TO LION MOUTH GROTTO

NEEDLE EYE CAVE: EXIT TO TREASURE CANYON

THE GIANT THUMB CAVE: EXIT TO GHOST EYE GORGE

SECRET CAVE: EXIT TO PINK STONE GORGE

GHOST EYE GORGE: EXIT TO THE GIANT THUMB CAVE

"Leo finally traced it to a series of desert caves, filled with winding passages and dead ends. He followed clue after clue, until he reached the last chamber."

Can you find the path Leo took through just ten caves to get to the chalice? You can crawl through the tunnels connecting the caves or go through the holes as directed. You can also find your own route.

In the chamber of chalices, the real chalice lies among many others. Can you see it?

CANDLE ROCK CAVERN: EXIT TO BAT CAVE

DARK BAT GROTTO: EXIT TO BROTHER CAVERN

TWIN CAVE: EXIT TO DEVIL EYE CAVE

BROTHER CAVERN: EXIT TO DARK BAT GROTTO

DOUBLE GATE GROTTO: EXIT TO SKULL GORGE

GREEN GATE CAVERN: EXIT TO ROSE QUARTZ CAVERN

BAT CAVE: EXIT TO CANDLE ROCK CAVERN

PINK STONE GORGE: EXIT TO SECRET CAVE

DRAGON CAVE: EXIT TO SENTINEL GROTTO

LION MOUTH GROTTO: EXIT TO PIRATE GORGE

FIRE-FLY CAVERN: EXIT TO BLUE GROTTO

MASK GROTTO: EXIT TO STALACTITE MAZE CAVERN

THE VALLEY OF THE DINOSAURS

"In the sixteenth century, armies of fierce invaders came to steal the treasures of South American Indians," says Jacob. "Just before these invaders attacked, one tribe managed to take their treasure into the high Andes, to the Valley of the Dinosaurs. There, they hid it in a cave, where it remained until Leo discovered it."

"How did he ever find it?" asks Susan.

"The Indians carved clues to its hiding place in the rocks," answers Jacob. "Leo followed these clues until he reached the cave. But just as he entered, the whole valley erupted in an earthquake. Leo grabbed as much of the treasure as he could. But the rest of it vanished forever, swallowed by the falling rocks."

The clues carved by the Indians were arrowheads. Each points to a cave—and some point to more than one cave. The treasure was hidden in the cave with the most arrowheads pointing to it. Can you find it? Leo also discovered signs of ten prehistoric animals hidden in the valley. Can you spot them?

LEO'S TROPICAL ISLAND MAP

"This map is a real puzzler," says Jacob. "It is supposed to have been drawn in 1661, but the experts think it is a fake."

"Then why is it in the exhibit?" asks Tom.

"Leo insisted on it," explains Jacob, taking off his cap to scratch his head. "He won't say why, but he hints that it is as important as anything else in the museum."

"But there's even a bit torn away," says Susan.

"And the end of the rhyme is missing," says Tom.

"Maybe the last part of the rhyme would have told us why the map is so important to Leo," says Matt.

Why do the experts think the map is a fake? Can you find twenty-five things that are wrong or that don't belong on a map of 1661? And can you work out the secret of the map without the torn piece? If not, don't worry. It will fall into place in the end.

The golden horde will fe re
when the secret is unsea
It's not on the island
It's not in the sea

TIME TO OPEN THE EXHIBIT!

Jacob and the children arrive back at the central hall of the museum. Once all the special guests arrive, Leo will open the exhibit by saying a few words.

"Thanks for telling us those great stories, Jacob," says Matt.

"Too bad we didn't find out the secret of the map," says Susan.

"Never mind," says Jacob, pulling a crumpled bit of paper from his pocket. "Let's see who's on Leo's special guest list."

Can you find all the special guests Leo has invited?

THE EMPEROR AND EMPRESS OF WAN TU

SIX CHEERLEADERS

FIVE WATUTSI

FIVE INDIAN LADIES WEARING SARIS

EIGHT MEMBERS OF THE AQUA CLUB

FOUR FRENCH CHEFS

THREE RUSSIAN BALLET DANCERS

"What's that on the back of the list?" asks Matt.

"It's the missing piece of Leo's map!" shouts Susan.

It's in the message surrounding me!

"Hurrah!" cries Tom. "Now we can solve the final mystery!"

Go back to Leo's map. Can you end the quest and discover the greatest treasure of the museum?

PUZZLE ANSWERS

Museum Quest

You can help Susan find her friends and reach Jacob by following the RED path. Tom, Matt, and Patches are circled in BLUE. Leo Panthera is circled in RED in this and all the other scenes.

Aztec Crystal Mystery

The BLUE path leads you all the way to the crystal lion's skull. The eleven wild animals are circled in RED and numbered as follows:

1. Poisonous frog
2. Armored lizard
3. Boa constrictor
4. Spider
5. Mosquito
6. Centipede
7. Alligator
8. Piranha
9. Lion
10. Scorpion
11. Vampire bat

The Twin Jade Lions of the Wan Tu

The two identical jade lions are circled in RED. The five Tongs are circled in BLUE. The banners that were changed are numbered one to four.

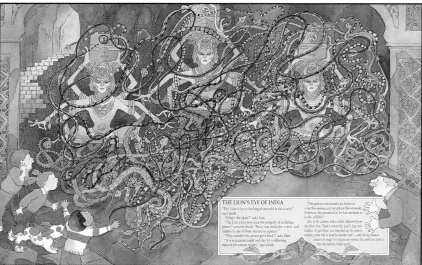

The Lion's Eye of India

The lion's eye is circled in BLUE. The BLUE path will take you through the snakes and up toward the statue. The RED path will take you back again.

The Treasure of the *Santa Morte*

Circled in RED are all the treasures of the *Santa Morte*. Here are ten things wrong with this picture, numbered as follows:

1. Snail shell on turtle
2. Square pearl
3. "Underwater" butterfly
4. Shark with three top fins
5. Octopus with nine legs
6. Shark with fangs
7. Jellyfish swimming the wrong way
8. "Deep-sea" frog
9. Upside-down fish
10. Crab with six legs

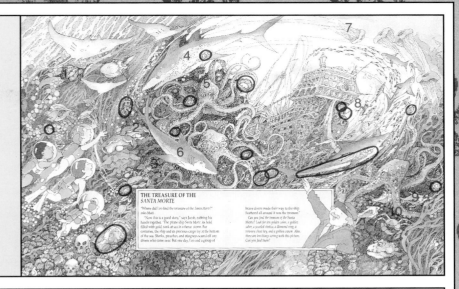

The Seven Diamonds of the Watutsi

The five Watutsi are circled in RED. The seven diamonds are shown in BLUE. Leo's clothes and belongings are circled in BLUE and numbered as follows:

1. Camera
2. Socks
3. Safari coat
4. Eye patch
5. Pants
6. Shoes
7. Shirt

The Lion Mask of Seti the Seventh

The thirteen black widow spiders are circled in BLUE. The duplicates of the twelve objects stolen by the tomb raiders are circled in RED.

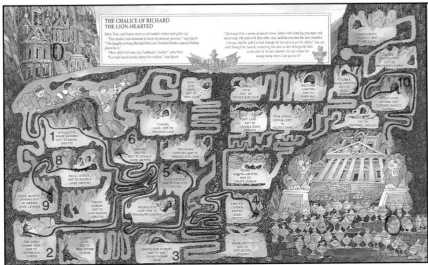

The Chalice of Richard the Lion-Hearted

The RED path takes you through the ten caves as numbered, leading you to the chamber of golden chalices. The real chalice is circled in BLUE.

The Valley of the Dinosaurs

The cave with the treasure is circled in BLUE. The ten prehistoric animals are outlined in RED and numbered as follows:

1. Parasaurolophus
2. Elasmosaurus
3. Tyrannosaurus
4. Allosaurus
5. Pterodactyl
6. Diplodocus
7. Triceratops
8. Hylaeosaurus
9. Stegosaurus
10. Camptosaurus

These figures will help you identify the prehistoric animals in the scene.

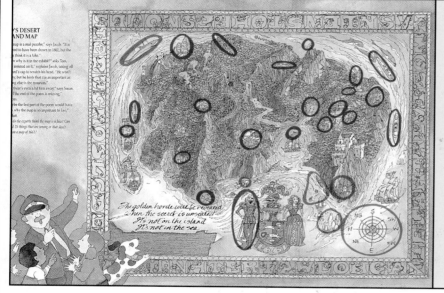

Leo's Tropical Island Map

Circled in BLUE are things wrong with this map. They are a shark with a whale's spout, a bird flying upside down, an octopus with ten legs, icebergs, alligators (they swim only in fresh water), and a mixed-up compass. Circled in RED are things that don't belong on a map of 1661. They are a water-skier, modern buildings, a helicopter, sunbathers with beach umbrellas, telephone poles and wires, a car, a telescope and observatory, a solar dish, a train on railroad tracks, a satellite pictured on a ship's flag, a hydroelectric dam, a U.S. flag, a rocket, a swimming pool, smokestacks, a submarine, an airplane, a football field, and an ocean liner. Can you find any more?

Time to Open the Exhibit!

The guests are circled and color coded as follows: Red, the Emperor and Empress of Wan Tu. Yellow, six cheerleaders. Blue, five Watutsi. Green, five Indian ladies. Purple, eight members of the Aqua Club. Black, four French chefs. Orange, three Russian ballet dancers. (Did you also spot the twelve security guards?)

To discover the greatest treasure of the museum, go back to Leo's map. Begin at the bottom left. Read every second letter surrounding the border of the map and you will discover this message: "The two great lions in the museum's central hall have manes of solid gold."